A **Literature Kit** FOR

# The Egypt Game

• • • • • • • • • • • • • • • • •

*By Zilpha Keatley Snyder*

Written by Nat Reed

## GRADES 5 – 6

**Classroom Complete Press**

P.O. Box 19729
San Diego, CA 92159
Tel: 1-800-663-3609 / Fax: 1-800-663-3608
Email: service@classroomcompletepress.com

**www.classroomcompletepress.com**

ISBN-13: 978-1-55319-335-7
ISBN-10: 1-55319-335-0

© 2006

# Critical Thinking Skills
## The Egypt Game

| Skills For Critical Thinking | | Chapter Questions | | | | | | | | | | Writing Tasks | Graphic Organizers |
|---|---|---|---|---|---|---|---|---|---|---|---|---|---|
| | | 1-2 | 3-4 | 5-7 | 8-9 | 10-12 | 13-14 | 15-17 | 18-19 | 20-21 | 22-23 | | |
| **LEVEL 1 Knowledge** | • Identify Story Elements | ✓ | ✓ | ✓ | ✓ | ✓ | ✓ | ✓ | ✓ | ✓ | ✓ | ✓ | ✓ |
| | • Recall Details | ✓ | ✓ | ✓ | ✓ | ✓ | ✓ | ✓ | ✓ | ✓ | ✓ | ✓ | ✓ |
| | • Match | ✓ | | ✓ | ✓ | ✓ | | ✓ | ✓ | ✓ | ✓ | ✓ | ✓ |
| | • Sequence | | ✓ | | | | ✓ | | | | ✓ | | ✓ |
| **LEVEL 2 Comprehension** | • Compare Characters | | | | ✓ | ✓ | ✓ | ✓ | ✓ | ✓ | | ✓ | |
| | • Summarize | ✓ | | ✓ | ✓ | ✓ | ✓ | ✓ | ✓ | ✓ | | ✓ | ✓ |
| | • State Main Idea | | | ✓ | | | | ✓ | | | | | ✓ |
| | • Describe | ✓ | ✓ | ✓ | ✓ | ✓ | ✓ | ✓ | ✓ | ✓ | ✓ | ✓ | |
| | • Classify | ✓ | | | | | ✓ | | | ✓ | ✓ | | ✓ |
| **LEVEL 3 Application** | • Plan | | | ✓ | | | ✓ | | | | ✓ | ✓ | ✓ |
| | • Interview | | | | | | ✓ | | | | | | |
| | • Infer Outcomes | | ✓ | ✓ | ✓ | | | ✓ | | ✓ | | | ✓ |
| **LEVEL 4 Analysis** | • Draw Conclusions | | ✓ | ✓ | ✓ | ✓ | ✓ | ✓ | ✓ | | ✓ | ✓ | ✓ |
| | • Identify Supporting Evidence | | ✓ | | | | | ✓ | ✓ | | | ✓ | ✓ |
| | • Infer Motivations | | ✓ | ✓ | ✓ | ✓ | | ✓ | ✓ | ✓ | ✓ | ✓ | ✓ |
| | • Identify Cause & Effect | | ✓ | ✓ | ✓ | | | ✓ | ✓ | ✓ | ✓ | ✓ | ✓ |
| **LEVEL 5 Synthesis** | • Predict | | ✓ | ✓ | ✓ | ✓ | ✓ | ✓ | ✓ | ✓ | ✓ | ✓ | ✓ |
| | • Design | | | ✓ | | | | | | | | ✓ | |
| | • Create | | ✓ | | | | ✓ | | | | | ✓ | ✓ |
| | • Imagine Alternatives | | | | | | | | ✓ | | | | |
| **LEVEL 6 Evaluation** | • Defend An Opinion | ✓ | ✓ | ✓ | ✓ | ✓ | ✓ | ✓ | ✓ | ✓ | ✓ | ✓ | ✓ |
| | • Make Judgements | ✓ | ✓ | ✓ | ✓ | ✓ | ✓ | ✓ | ✓ | ✓ | ✓ | ✓ | ✓ |

*Based on Bloom's Taxonomy*

# Contents

## 🍎 TEACHER GUIDE

## ✏️ STUDENT HANDOUTS

---

✔ **6 BONUS Activity Pages!** Additional worksheets for your students
✔ **3 BONUS Overhead Transparencies!** For use with your projection system

**FREE!**

- Go to our website: **www.classroomcompletepress.com/bonus**
- Enter item CC2503 or The Egypt Game
- Enter pass code CC2503D for Activity Pages. CC2503A for Overheads.

# Assessment Rubric

## The Egypt Game

Student's Name: _____

Assignment: _____

Level: _____

| | Level 1 | Level 2 | Level 3 | Level 4 |
|---|---|---|---|---|
| **Comprehension of the Novel** | Demonstrates a limited understanding of the novel | Demonstrates a basic understanding of the novel | Demonstrates a good understanding of the novel | Demonstrates a thorough understanding of the novel |
| **Content** | Information incomplete; key details missing | Some information complete; details missing | All required information complete; key details contain some description | All required information complete; enough description for clarity |
| **Style** | Little variety in word choice; language vague and imprecise | Some variety in word choice; language somewhat vague and imprecise | Good variety in word choice; language precise and quite descriptive | Writer's voice is apparent throughout. Excellent choice of words; precise language. |
| **Conventions** | Errors seriously interfere with the writer's purpose | Repeated errors in mechanics and usage | Some errors in convention | Few errors in convention |

**STRENGTHS:**

**WEAKNESSES:**

**NEXT STEPS:**

# Teacher Guide

## This resource has been created for ease of use by both TEACHERS and STUDENTS alike.

### Introduction

**Z**ilpha Keatley Snyder's novel, **The Egypt Game**, has proven to be tremendously popular with young people around the world. A Newbery Honor winner, this is the highly imaginative and lively adventure of a group of friends who share a fascination for ancient Egypt. Teeming with suspense and humor, the novel explores the themes of Egypt and its remarkable history, the ancient pharaohs, pyramids and burial ceremonies, ancient Egyptian gods and goddesses, magic and mythology. Other themes are those of friendship, parental relationships, prejudices based on appearance or first impressions, personal insecurities and responsibilities.

### How Is This Literature Kit™ Organized?

#### STUDENT HANDOUTS

**Chapter Activities** (in the form of reproducible worksheets) make up the majority of this resource. For each chapter or group of chapters there are BEFORE YOU READ activities and AFTER YOU READ activities.

- The BEFORE YOU READ activities prepare students for reading by setting a purpose for reading. They stimulate background knowledge and experience, and guide students to make connections between what they know and what they will learn. Important concepts and vocabulary from the chapter(s) are also presented.

- The AFTER YOU READ activities check students' comprehension and extend their learning. Students are asked to give thoughtful consideration of the text through creative and evaluative short-answer questions and journal prompts.

Six **Writing Tasks** and three **Graphic Organizers** are included to further develop students' critical thinking and writing skills, and analysis of the text. (*See page 6 for suggestions on using the Graphic Organizers.*) The **Assessment Rubric** (*page 4*) is a useful tool for evaluating students' responses to the Writing Tasks and Graphic Organizers.

### PICTURE CUES

This resource contains three main types of pages, each with a different purpose and use. A **Picture Cue** at the top of each page shows, at a glance, what the page is for.

 **Teacher Guide**
- Information and tools for the teacher

 **Student Handout**
- Reproducible worksheets and activities

 **Easy Marking™ Answer Key**
- Answers for student activities

### EASY MARKING™ ANSWER KEY

Marking students' worksheets is fast and easy with this **Answer Key**. Answers are listed in columns – just line up the column with its corresponding worksheet, as shown, and see how every question matches up with its answer!

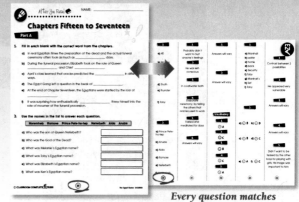

*Every question matches up with its answer!*

# 1,2,3
## Graphic Organizer Transparencies

The three **Graphic Organizer Transparencies** included in this Literature Kit™ are especially suited to a study of **The Egypt Game**. Below are suggestions for using each organizer in your classroom, or they may be adapted to suit the individual needs of your students. The transparencies can be used on an overhead projector in teacher-led activities, and/or photocopied for use as student worksheets. To evaluate students' responses to any of the organizers, you may wish to use the **Assessment Rubric** (on page 4).

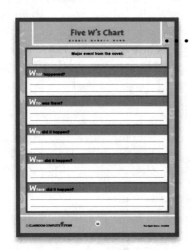

### FIVE W'S CHART

In *The Egypt Game*, the author has skillfully brought to life an unusual cast of characters with detailed characterizations and settings, and a richly developed plot. The Five W's Chart is an excellent tool to help students identify and analyze these literary elements. Students are to choose one major event from the novel and give the key details about what happened, who was there, when and where it happened, and why the event unfolded as it did. This chart may also be used as a planning activity to help students develop their skills in writing a research article. **Found on Page 53.**

### SEQUENCE CHART

To begin this activity, ask students what they think are the six most important events of the novel. Have them record their ideas on a separate sheet of paper, and then transcribe the events onto the Sequence Chart in the order that they occurred in the plot. For each event, a brief description should be given and at least one reason why each was essential to the plot. A variety of answers are possible for this activity; teachers should look for a logical rationale to the question, "Why was this event essential to the plot?" **Found on Page 54.**

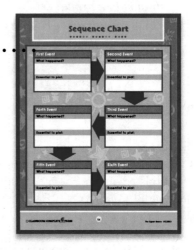

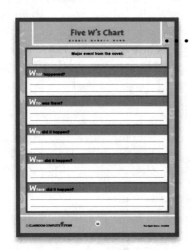

### KWL CHART

The KWL Chart is a useful tool to help students develop their skills in planning and writing a nonfiction article. After having an initial discussion, ask students to brainstorm topics related to ancient Egypt for further investigation (i.e., mummies, pyramids, Egyptian gods and goddesses, pharaohs, etc.). Working individually or in pairs, have students choose one topic from the list to research. Then, they are to jot down what they already know about the topic, and list several points about what they would like to learn. Have students conduct their research, and record the information they found (what they learned). **Found on Page 55.**

# Bloom's Taxonomy* for Reading Comprehension

The activities in this resource engage and build the full range of thinking skills that are essential for students' reading comprehension. Based on the six levels of thinking in Bloom's Taxonomy, questions are given that challenge students to not only recall what they have read, but move beyond this to understand the text through higher-order thinking. By using higher-order skills of application, analysis, synthesis and evaluation, students become active readers, drawing more meaning from the text, and applying and extending their learning in more sophisticated ways.

This Literature Kit™, therefore, is an effective tool for any Language Arts program. Whether it is used in whole or in part, or adapted to meet individual student needs, this resource provides teachers with the important questions to ask, inspiring students' interest, creativity, and promoting meaningful learning.

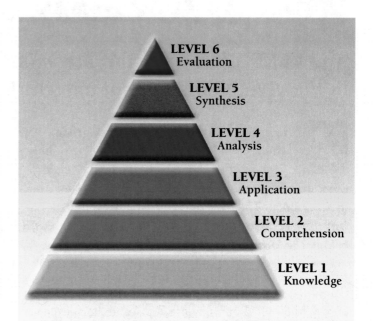

**BLOOM'S TAXONOMY:
6 LEVELS OF THINKING**

*Bloom's Taxonomy is a widely used tool by educators for classifying learning objectives, and is based on the work of Benjamin Bloom.*

## Teaching Strategies — WHOLE-CLASS, SMALL GROUP AND INDEPENDENT STUDY

***The Egypt Game*** is a novel that may be approached in several ways. Most obvious is as a traditional, whole-class read-aloud in which the teacher reads the book out loud to the entire class, stopping after one or more chapters for the students to answer the chapter questions. As they complete the questions, students reread the chapter(s) on their own. Depending on the interests and needs of your students, you may choose to apply some shared or modeled reading, focusing discussion on the author's skills, choices made in writing, and the elements of the narrative. The BEFORE YOU READ and AFTER YOU READ activities in this Literature Kit™ provide a basis for such discussions.

To facilitate small group and independent study learning, these activities have been divided into chapter groupings to allow students to work on manageable sections of the novel, and not feel overwhelmed by the activities. Teachers may also choose to use only a selection of the activities in this resource for small group or independent study, assigning tasks that match students' specific needs, and allowing students to work at their own speed. The components of this resource make it flexible and easy to adapt as not all of the activities need to be completed.

Teachers may wish to have their students keep a daily reading log so that they might record their daily progress and reflections. Journaling prompts have been included at the end of each chapter section to facilitate students' thinking and writing.

# Summary of the Story

## A LIVELY adventure story, teeming with suspense and humor, and set in the vivid landscapes of ancient Egypt and modern-day California.

**A**pril Hall is not your typical sixth grade student, and when she goes to live with her grandmother, her new best friend, Melanie Ross, dreads the day when April will begin school in September. The lives of the girls, however, are transformed when they convert a deserted storage yard behind the local antique shop into the land of Egypt.

*Egypt* is owned by the mysterious Professor, who turns a blind eye to the activities going on in his backyard. Limited only by their vivid imaginations, April and Melanie create the Egypt Game, which grows more and more complex and interesting. Finally, other children from the neighborhood are drawn into the Game including the two most popular boys in their class – Toby and Ken.

It is in this enchanted land that the Egypt Gang spin an imaginative web of intrigue involving mysterious oracles, messages in hieroglyphics, ancient Egyptian names, and forbidden ceremonies.

When a child from the neighborhood is mysteriously murdered, however, the Egypt Game takes a deadly turn, almost costing April her life.

At the novel's conclusion, it is the Professor, himself, who comes to the rescue, saving April and Egypt itself. In the process, the Professor reveals his colorful past to the Gang and presents them with their own personal keys to the land of Egypt.

## Suggestions for Further Reading

### BOOKS BY ZILPHA KEATLEY SNYDER
*The Velvet Room* © 1965
*Black and Blue Magic* © 1966
*The Changeling* © 1970
*The Headless Cupid* © 1971
*The Witches of Worm* © 1972
*Below the Root* © 1975
*And All Between* © 1976
*The Gypsy Game* © 1997
*Gib and the Gray Ghost* © 2000
*The Ghosts of Rathburn Park* © 2002
*The Unseen* © 2004
*The Magic Nation Thing* © 2005
*The Treasures of Weatherby* © 2006

### OTHER RECOMMENDED RESOURCES
C. S. Lewis, *The Lion, the Witch and the Wardrobe* © 1950
Eloise Jarvis McGraw, *Mara, Daughter of the Nile* © 1953
Eloise Jarvis McGraw, *The Golden Goblet* © 1961
Madeleine L'Engle, *A Wrinkle in Time* © 1962
Elizabeth Payne, *Pharaohs of Ancient Egypt* ©1964
Katherine Paterson, *Bridge to Terabithia* © 1977
Ellen Raskin, *The Westing Game* © 1978
Ludmila Zeman, *Revenge of Ishtar* ©1998

# Vocabulary

**CHAPTERS 1 AND 2**
• antique • ancestor • vague • dingy • inspired • prospect • gunnysack • straggly • residents • security • reproduction • taut • refinement • improvise • inspiration • dramatically • curtsy • frantic • dignity • righteous

**CHAPTERS 3 AND 4**
• apt • elaborate • drastic • evasive • associate • warily • intend • adjust • inform • showboating • interrupt • revenge • criminal • haughtiness • tragic • romance • fascinate • sympathetic • hieroglyphics • accumulate • monolith • pharaoh • complicated • integrate • exploration

**CHAPTERS 5 TO 7**
• corrugated • atmosphere • apparently • heir • authority • obliged • suspiciously • defiantly • brimstone • treacherous • triumph • papyrus • figurine • crinoline • sacrificial • prostration • sympathy • enchanted • ferocious • delicate • ambushed

**CHAPTERS 8 AND 9**
• ceremony • clamored • languishing • dungeon • clutches • balconies • circumstance • medley • theories • predictable • tunic • apparently • atmosphere • splendors • occasional • frustratingly • vulture • chaperoned • scheme • tendency

**CHAPTERS 10 TO 12**
• unwieldy • wilt • convinced • momentum • exasperated • swiveled • liable • sculptor • deodorant • convulsions • rehearsed • unison • tailspin • incense • infested • dignity • unpatriotic • prostrated • philosophically • mournful • console • shred • haughty

**CHAPTERS 13 AND 14**
• restricted • exaggerated • mugged • suspicious • reluctant • balefully • tarantula • decipher • investigation • exchanged • captive • crummy • doom • ornaments • altar • flattered • scroll • soothing • cooped • condition

**CHAPTERS 15 TO 17**
• previous • rendezvous • elaborating • gratifyingly • dahlias • populace • sophisticated • bier • dispense • pomp • mummification • queasy • grottoes • mystic • prediction • consternation • oracle • exalted • fasting • elaborate • regal

**CHAPTERS 18 AND 19**
• pester • impatience • university • assistantship • reality • cinch • parallel • impression • indignantly • definitely • hesitantly • incredulous • paralyzed • resign • jet-propelled • quotation • fishy • anxious • disguise

**CHAPTERS 20 AND 21**
• enthusiastic • exasperated • exaggerate • disturbing • theory • reasonable • mysterious • ridiculous • slither • hoarse • inspector • commotion • confusion • transferred • wearily • obediently • vividly • situation • alibi • detective • bewildered • criminally

**CHAPTERS 22 AND 23**
• scarcely • consensus • particular • seclusion • lair • mourn • squatted • tension • artistically • consciences • verge • alabaster • Egyptologist • sequins • speculated • fiercest • intriguing • optimistic • anthropology • eliminating • intent • obligated • Gypsies • primitive

# Zilpha Keatley Snyder

**With the examples of her parents to guide her, Zilpha became an imaginitive storyteller at a young age.**

**B**orn in 1927, Zilpha Keatley Snyder was raised in rural California. Raised without television, her childhood was filled with pets of all shapes and sizes. With the examples of her parents to guide her, she became an imaginative storyteller at a young age.

When she entered seventh grade, Zilpha began to feel that she was a terrible misfit, and retreated into the world of books and imagination. This retreat would eventually stand her in good stead a few years later, when she began to spin some of the most creative characters and plotlines in young people's literature.

Zilpha attended Whittier College in southern California where she met her future husband, Larry Snyder. Married in 1950, she and her husband had three children. After finishing school, Zilpha taught school for nine years and it wasn't until her children were all in school that she finally began to entertain the idea of writing.

Zilpha has written for both adults and children, but she is happiest writing novels for young people. It is in crafting these stories that her own character, namely her boundless optimism, natural curiosity, and freewheeling imagination, shines through.

## Did You Know?

- Zilpha's first novel, <u>Season of Ponies</u>, was based on a dream and was published in 1964.
- Zilpha is a three-time Newbery Honor winner!
    * <u>The Egypt Game</u>
    * <u>The Headless Cupid</u>
    * <u>The Witches of Worm</u>
- Zilpha has written over 40 books, including novels, poems and picture books.

# Chapters One and Two

**Answer the questions in complete sentences.**

**1.** Describe the most interesting store you have ever been in. What features of the store made it so fascinating?

_____

_____

**2.** Describe the most interesting person you have ever met. You may choose an individual who was interesting-looking, or had a fascinating personality.

_____

_____

## Vocabulary

**Complete each sentence with a word from the list.**

| innovation | improvise | vantage | exotic | deadpan | dingy | taut |
|---|---|---|---|---|---|---|

**1.** My grandfather lived in a dark, _____ apartment that was located above an antique shop.

**2.** We all pulled on the rope until it was very _____.

**3.** A simple _____ to the scientist's experiment ended up being worth millions of dollars.

**4.** When the actress forgot her lines, she was forced to _____.

**5.** The owner of the antique shop gave April and Melanie a blank, _____ expression that the girls found impossible to read.

**6.** There's no doubt that my friend's pet parrot was the most _____ - looking animal at the school pet show.

**7.** The guard was forced to leave his _____ place by the window when it began to rain.

NAME: _____

# Chapters One and Two

## Part A

**Put a check mark next to the answer that is most correct.**

**1.** **Which words best describe the personality of the Professor?**
- ○ **A** quiet and mysterious
- ○ **B** talkative and outgoing
- ○ **C** nasty and violent
- ○ **D** sarcastic and hurtful

**2.** **What was the setting of the very beginning of The Egypt Game?**
- ○ **A** April's back yard
- ○ **B** the laundry room of April's apartment building
- ○ **C** the storage yard of an antique shop
- ○ **D** an empty lot beside Melanie's apartment building

**3.** **What is the sacred flower of Egypt?**
- ○ **A** the lotus blossom
- ○ **B** the lilac blossom
- ○ **C** the yellow rose
- ○ **D** the pink carnation

**4.** **April believed that in an earlier reincarnation she was a:**
- ○ **A** servant girl
- ○ **B** sorceress
- ○ **C** princess
- ○ **D** high priestess

**5.** **What did April plan on becoming when she grew up?**
- ○ **A** an actress
- ○ **B** a museum curator
- ○ **C** an archaeologist
- ○ **D** a theologian

# Chapters One and Two

## Part B

**Answer the questions in complete sentences.**

**1.**  a) Why do you think it was so appropriate that the Professor owned an antique store?

_____

b) Choose three adjectives that aptly describe the Professor's appearance or personality.

_____

**2.**  Describe the personality of the following characters using one sentence for each description: April, Caroline, Marshall, Melanie, Dorthea.

_____

_____

_____

**3.**  The first two chapters feature at least two examples of **foreshadowing** (a hint of something coming up in the story). In Chapter One the author writes, **"The Professor happened to be the only witness to the very beginning of the Egypt Game"**. This statement arouses our interest in the Egypt Game and what the game might be all about. Another example of foreshadowing is found in Chapter Two: **"It was almost as if the old man's deadly silence was a dangerous dark hole . . ."** How is this statement an example of foreshadowing?

_____

_____

**4.**  A **simile** is a comparison of two objects using the words like or as. Find an example of a simile in the description of the Professor in Chapter One, or the description of him in Chapter Two.

_____

**Journal Activity**

**Now that you have finished the first two chapters of the novel, tell how you think the Egypt Game will come about. How do you think it will come into being, and what will the game be like? Give as many details as possible.**

# Chapters Three and Four

**Answer the questions in complete sentences.**

**1.** What would you find most interesting about an antique shop? Be specific.

_____

_____

**2.** Describe one thing in the behavior of another student your age that most young people would find offensive. Why do you think people find this type of behavior so objectionable?

_____

_____

## Vocabulary

**With a straight line, connect each word on the left with its meaning on the right.**

|  |  | |  | |
|---|------|---|---------|---|
| 1 | apt | | proud | A |
| 2 | wary | | sad | B |
| 3 | revenge | | make into a whole | C |
| 4 | haughty | | investigation | D |
| 5 | tragic | | vague | E |
| 6 | sympathetic | | severe | F |
| 7 | accumulate | | harder | G |
| 8 | complicated | | get even | H |
| 9 | drastic | | compassionate | I |
| 10 | evasive | | likely | J |
| 11 | integrate | | cautious | K |
| 12 | exploration | | collect | L |

# Chapters Three and Four

**Part A**

1. **Circle** **T** if the statement is TRUE or **F** if it is FALSE.

T  F  **a)** April and her mother were a lot alike in some ways.

T  F  **b)** April was good at figuring out what adults meant by the things they didn't quite say.

T  F  **c)** April would have nothing to do with Melanie's paper dolls.

T  F  **d)** April's vivid imagination was a constant source of annoyance to Melanie.

T  F  **e)** Melanie didn't want April to wear her fake eyelashes to school.

T  F  **f)** Both Melanie and April were avid readers.

2. **Number the events from 1 to 6 in the order they occurred in the chapters.**

_____ **a)** Melanie and April both begin to worry about the first day of school.

_____ **b)** April finds out about Melanie's paper doll collection.

_____ **c)** Melanie goes to April's apartment to invite her to lunch.

_____ **d)** April tells Melanie and her family about her mother, Dorthea, being a movie star.

_____ **e)** The girls find the deserted yard where the Egypt Game began.

_____ **f)** Melanie shows April her library.

NAME: _____

# Chapters Three and Four

## Part B

**Answer the questions in complete sentences.**

**1.** April is a most unusual character. Give proof from the story to show that April was unusual in the following areas: the way she dressed (her appearance), and the way she sometimes talked.

_____

_____

**2.** Give a realistic appraisal of Dorthea's acting career.

_____

_____

**3.** What does the following statement tell you about Melanie's personality: **"You just had to let her (April) know she couldn't make you stop liking her that easily"?**

_____

_____

**4.** Chapter Four contains an example of **personification** (writing about inanimate objects as if they were a person): **The plank "had moved stiffly . . . with a rusty yelp."** Create a sentence using this literary device personifying a car or truck.

_____

**5.** Melanie comes to the conclusion that April wouldn't be easy to **"trim down to size"** by the students at Wilson School. From what you know about April, do you agree or disagree with Melanie? Defend your answer.

_____

**Journal Activity**

**Describe the most unusual person you have ever known. What was there about this individual that made him or her memorable to you?**

# Chapters Five to Seven

1. If you were a part of the Egypt Game, what are two things you might change or bring to the storage yard to make it more like an Egyptian temple?

   _____

   _____

2. In order for April and Melanie to have an enjoyable and successful time playing the Egypt Game, what do you think would be necessary for them to do in preparation?

   _____

   _____

## Vocabulary

**Complete each sentence with a word from the list.**

| ferocious | delicate | treacherous | ambushed | sympathy | obliged | defiant |

1. April felt _____ to be kind to her grandmother, even though she felt alone some of the time.

2. Marshall was a quiet boy, but could be quite _____ when he felt he was being picked on.

3. The trail up the mountainside was very _____.

4. Our teacher didn't have any _____ for students who were caught cheating.

5. The _____ black bear charged across the field toward the children.

6. Melanie's figurine of Nefertiti was extremely _____, so we had to handle it with care.

7. The two boys hid behind the thick bush and _____ April and Melanie as they passed.

# Chapters Five to Seven

## Part A

**1.** **Fill in each blank with the correct word from the chapters.**

**a)** The evil god of the Egyptian world was called _____.

**b)** Marshall's Egyptian name was _____, the boy pharaoh.

**c)** Toby and Ken nicknamed April, _____.

**d)** The _____ Stone became the mysterious and powerful source of much of Set's power.

**e)** Elizabeth was only in grade _____.

**f)** Melanie's father, Mr. Ross, taught _____ and literature at a local college.

## Vocabulary

**2.** **Answer each question with a word from the list.**

| Diana | Casa Rosada | Security | papyrus | Nefertiti |
|-------|-------------|----------|---------|-----------|

**a)** The ancient people of Egypt made their paper from this.

**b)** Melanie's profile reminded the girls of this Egyptian goddess.

**c)** What was the name of Marshall's octopus?

**d)** The Egyptians stored their sacred records in the wooden base of a statue of this Egyptian god.

**e)** What was the name of April's apartment building?

After You Read

# Chapters Five to Seven

## Part B

**Answer the questions in complete sentences.**

**1.** Read again the last paragraph of Chapter Five. Describe the mood that the author wishes to convey. How is she able to accomplish this?

_____

**2.** Put the following sentence into your own words: **"Melanie had a hard time trying to translate April into something that Wilson School could understand and appreciate."**

_____

_____

**3.** Do you think it would benefit Melanie if April was accepted and liked by the other students at Wilson School? Defend your answer.

_____

_____

**4.** When Melanie took one of April's eyelashes she felt **"triumphant and treacherous at the same time"**. Explain why you think she felt this way.

_____

**5.** April is certainly a unique character. Imagine she joined your class as a new student. Think of one possible advantage and one disadvantage to having April as a member of your class.

_____

_____

**In Chapter Six April makes the statement, "Yeah, I guess everybody has something they're not very grown up about". Write a personal reflection about this statement. You may wish to think of yourself as an adult; what do you think you will still enjoy doing then that you presently enjoying doing?**

# Chapters Eight and Nine

**1.** What advantage might there be in including more people in the Egypt Game? What might be a disadvantage?

_____

_____

## Vocabulary

**Word List**

| | | |
|---|---|---|
| CEREMONY | KURGAN | HAUNT |
| ULU | OWED | NOON |
| TUNIC | IT | CLAMOR |
| ANTIQUE | LOGICAL | DISMAY |
| SMILE | WHY | ROSADA |
| DRAMAS | BALCONY | FROM |
| CHAPERON | IMITATES | IDOL |
| OMEN | CURIOUS | RAPT |
| SPREAD | OILY | BY |
| MISTAKE | | |

## Down

1. "Where are you ___?"
2. Near
3. Loud noise
4. Nosy
5. Error
6. Midday
7. Ancient relic
11. A kind of knife
12. Guardian
14. Copies
16. Deeply absorbed
18. A false god
21. To be indebted
22. One of the 5 W's
24. He, she and __

## Across

2. Outside part of an apartment
4. Formal function
8. Serious narrative works
9. A sign of the future
10. Egyptian garment
13. Sensible
15. A city in Russia
17. Opposite of *frown*
19. Stretch or widen
20. The *Casa* _____
23. Greasy
25. A visit by ghosts
26. Sorrow

# Chapters Eight and Nine

## Part A

**1.** **Complete the paragraphs with the correct words from the chapters.**

One afternoon the Egypt Game was interrupted by Mrs. _____. She informed
____a____
the group that a little _____ in the neighborhood had been _____.
____b____                                              ____c____
Police suspected the guilty person was a resident of the _____. In the days
____d____
following this tragedy, all there was left to do for the boys and girls of the area was to

_____. Melanie thought that people commit such crimes because they're
____e____

_____. One person who appeared to be a suspect was the_____,
____f____                                                                    ____g____
although the Egypt Gang thought he was _____.
____h____

The girls explained that they were making Egyptian costumes because _____
____i____
wasn't far away.  Visiting the Egypt Place on Halloween might be downright _____
____j____
and deadly _____.  For Halloween, April had her hair cut in a _____
____k____                                                              ____l____
bob.  Before leaving for Egypt, Marshall returned to his bedroom for _____.
____m____

**2.** **Which answer best describes...**

**a) Alice?**

  ○ **A** imaginative
  ○ **B** shy
  ○ **C** quiet
  ○ **D** dull

**b) the response of the neighbors to the tragedy?**

  ○ **A** didn't really care
  ○ **B** fear and concern
  ○ **C** ignored the incident
  ○ **D** tried to track down the guilty person

**c) April's feelings about being kept out of Egypt?**

  ○ **A** didn't care
  ○ **B** liked the idea
  ○ **C** hated the idea
  ○ **D** thought it was silly

**d) who thought the Professor was innocent?**

  ○ **A** Caroline
  ○ **B** most of the neighborhood
  ○ **C** the Egypt Gang
  ○ **D** only Marshall

# Chapters Eight and Nine

## Part B

**Answer the questions in complete sentences.**

**1.** It mentions in Chapter Nine that April struck a **"wonder-and-amazement pose"**. Describe how you visualize such a pose to look.

_____

_____

**2.** Melanie observes that despite April's sophisticated ways, most of her information seemed to be the kind grown-ups let you overhear, or what you find in the children's library. What do you think this reveals about April's upbringing?

_____

_____

**3.** Why do you think the Egypt Gang found it so difficult to believe the Professor was the killer?

_____

_____

**4.** Why do you think Dorthea refused to answer April's questions about when April could come home?

_____

_____

**5.** Why do you think Melanie was so relieved to see that April had changed her hair style on Halloween evening?

_____

**Journal Activity**

These two chapters introduce a rather sobering note to the novel, upsetting not only the Egypt Game, but the entire neighborhood. Describe an incident in your own life that this tragedy reminded you of. Tell about how you felt and how others around you acted during this time.

NAME: _____

# Chapters Ten to Twelve

**Answer the questions in complete sentences.**

**1.** How do you think the girls will get back into Egypt?

_____

_____

_____

**2.** Define **diplomacy**. Give an example of diplomacy in action.

_____

_____

_____

## Vocabulary

**Choose a word from the list that means the same or nearly the same as the underlined word.**

| liable | prostrated | unwieldy | shred | convulsions | together | haughty |

**1.** April found the sword to be very **awkward**.

**2.** The princess gave the poor peasant a **proud** look.

**3.** The girls burst into **fits** of laughter at the very thought.

**4.** You're **likely** to get hurt if you continue to be so careless.

**5.** The twins spoke their parts in the play **in unison**.

**6.** The Egypt Gang **bowed** low before the statue of Isis.

**7.** She left a **piece** of her fingernail as a sacrifice.

# Chapters Ten to Twelve

## Part A

**Put a check mark next to the answer that is most correct.**

1. **Toby had a special talent for getting people off the hook. How did he usually accomplish this?**
   - ○ **A**   by making the teacher laugh
   - ○ **B**   by taking the blame himself
   - ○ **C**   by telling one of his famous "tall tales"
   - ○ **D**   by pleading the case of others

2. **Toby was dressed up as a:**
   - ○ **A**   monster
   - ○ **B**   pharaoh
   - ○ **C**   box man
   - ○ **D**   nothing

3. **The sacred symbol of Set was:**
   - ○ **A**   the Altar of Thor
   - ○ **B**   the Crocodile Stone
   - ○ **C**   the Oak of Mamre
   - ○ **D**   the Blood of Sacrifices

4. **Which word best describes Toby's reaction to Elizabeth's invitation to join the Egypt Game?**
   - ○ **A**   scorn
   - ○ **B**   ridicule
   - ○ **C**   interest
   - ○ **D**   disinterest

5. **Which word best describes the girls' reaction to Ken and Toby joining the Egypt Game?**
   - ○ **A**   dismay
   - ○ **B**   joy
   - ○ **C**   rage
   - ○ **D**   eagerness

# Chapters Ten to Twelve

## Part B

**Answer the questions in complete sentences.**

**1.** What do you think is meant by the statement, **"Ken Kamata and Toby Alvillar were just about the most disgusting boys in the sixth grade, in a fascinating sort of way"**?

_____

_____

**2.** In Chapter Ten the author uses a **simile** (a comparison of two things using the words like or as) to compare Toby's eyes to **"a pair of TV screens turned on full blast"**. Use this literary device to describe the following items:

a) April's hair _____

b) The Professor's shop _____

**3.** What do you think Marshall meant in Chapter Eleven when he said, **"somebody already heard us"**?

_____

_____

**4.** Put the following statement in your own words: **"Kamata and Alvillar were two guys who weren't easy to confuse"**.

_____

_____

**5.** Describe both Ken and Toby's reaction to Elizabeth's invitation to join the game.

_____

_____

**Journal Activity** — **Imagine you are either Ken or Toby. Write a journal entry describing how you feel about joining the Egypt Game.**

# Chapters Thirteen and Fourteen

**Answer the questions in complete sentences.**

**1.** A person's name is a very important part of one's identity. Investigate your own name (either your given name or surname) and relate one important fact about it (for example, its meaning, or how you came by it).

_____

_____

**2.** Hieroglyphics (word pictures) are one of civilization's first attempts at a workable alphabet. Give one advantage that our alphabet probably has over Egyptian hieroglyphics.

_____

_____

## Vocabulary

**Choose a word from the list that means the same or nearly the same as the underlined word.**

| hesitant | inquiry | exchanged | aggravated | plain | decipher | tragic |
|---|---|---|---|---|---|---|

**1.** Alice wore an **exasperated** expression when she read the letter.

**2.** It was **obvious** that Ken did not like the game as much as Toby.

**3.** My brother was very **reluctant** to give away his birthday present.

**4.** I wept when I heard the **sad** story.

**5.** Only a very smart person would be able to **figure out** the code.

**6.** We **traded** baseball cards during recess.

**7.** The police decided to launch an **investigation** into the murder.

# Chapters Thirteen and Fourteen

## Part A

1. **Circle T** if the statement is **TRUE** or **F** if it is **FALSE**.

   **T  F**  **a)** The inspiration for Toby's costume came from his dad.

   **T  F**  **b)** April's mother, Dorthea, wrote to say that she had gotten married.

   **T  F**  **c)** Caroline was very unsympathetic to April when she received the letter from her mother.

   **T  F**  **d)** Ken chose "Thoth" as his Egyptian name.

   **T  F**  **e)** <u>Aida</u> was the tragic story of a beautiful princess who'd been held captive in ancient Egypt.

   **T  F**  **f)** Elizabeth's Egyptian name came from the name Nefertiti.

2. **Number the events from ❶ to ❻ in the order they occurred in the chapters.**

   _____  **a)** Melanie's parents agree to let her play outdoors again.

   _____  **b)** April receives a letter from Dorthea.

   _____  **c)** Toby gets the girls to give him the names of some of the best books about Egypt.

   _____  **d)** The boys bring several props to use in the Egypt Game.

   _____  **e)** The gang chooses Egyptian names for themselves.

   _____  **f)** Petey the parakeet is killed by the neighbor's cat.

# Chapters Thirteen and Fourteen

## Part B

**Answer the questions in complete sentences.**

1. The author writes, **"Toby mugged an exaggerated exasperated look . . ."** The word **mug** can be used as a **verb** (as it is in this sentence) or as a **noun** (for example, the *coffee mug was broken.*) Use the word **plant** in two different sentences, first as a noun, then a verb.

   _____

   _____

2. What was there about Dorthea's letter that upset April so much?

   _____

   _____

3. What did April mean by this statement: **"Thinking how long it had been since she'd cried enough to taste"**?

   _____

   _____

4. Chapter Thirteen contains an example of the literary device, **onomatopoeia** (using sound words – for example, **"whirr-clank-buzz"**). Find two more examples of this literary device and indicate what each might refer to.

   _____

   _____

5. What props did the boys contribute to the Egypt Game?

   _____

**Journal Activity**

April's mother seems to be a very self-centered person and does not really consider her daughter's feelings very often. People like Dorthea are usually difficult to tolerate. Describe a time in your own life when you were hurt in a similar way to April in these chapters. Describe the circumstances and how you felt.

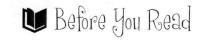 
# Chapters Fifteen to Seventeen

**1.** Define **oracle**. Give your impression as to whether you think such a thing is possible.

_____

_____

_____

**2.** Define **mystery**. Why do you think mysteries often make for interesting stories?

_____

_____

_____

## Vocabulary

**Use each of the following words in a complete sentence. (You may need to use a dictionary for some of the words.) Make the meaning of each word clear from the context of the sentence.**

**1. previous**  _____

**2. gratifying**  _____

**3. sophisticated**  _____

**4. dispense**  _____

**5. pomp**  _____

**6. queasy**  _____

**7. grottoes**  _____

**8. consternation**  _____

NAME: _____

# Chapters Fifteen to Seventeen

## Part A

**1.** **Fill in each blank with the correct word from the chapters.**

**a)** In real Egyptian times the preparation of the dead and the actual funeral ceremony often took as much as _____ days.

**b)** During the funeral procession, Elizabeth took on the role of Queen _____ and Chief _____.

**c)** April's class learned that oracles predicted the _____ in different ways.

**d)** The Egypt Gang left a question in the beak of _____.

**e)** At the end of Chapter Seventeen, the Egyptians were startled by the roar of _____.

**f)** It was surprising how enthusiastically _____ threw himself into the role of mourner at the funeral procession.

**2.** **Use the names in the list to answer each question.**

| Horemheb | Ramose | Prince Pete-ho-tep | Neferbeth | Aida | Anubis |
|---|---|---|---|---|---|

**a)** Who was the son of Queen Neferbeth? 

**b)** Who was the God of the Dead? 

**c)** What was Melanie's Egyptian name? 

**d)** What was Toby's Egyptian name? 

**e)** What was Elizabeth's Egyptian name? 

**f)** What was Ken's Egyptian name?

# Chapters Fifteen to Seventeen

**Part B**

**Answer the questions in complete sentences.**

**1.** Why do you think Elizabeth found it difficult to choose the high priest?

_____

_____

**2.** Why did Ken find it difficult to be a part of the funeral procession?

_____

_____

**3.** How did they decide to "mummify" Prince Pete-ho-tep's body?

_____

_____

**4.** What did Toby do and say to help convince the others that Thoth might actually answer their questions?

_____

_____

**5.** According to April, how did the people who were going to the oracle prepare themselves?

_____

_____

**6.** Think of two possible explanations for the source of the answer to Ken's question.

_____

_____

**Journal Activity**

**Describe a time in your life when you lost someone close to you. Describe your feelings and what helped you to recover.**

# Chapters Eighteen and Nineteen

**Answer the questions in complete sentences.**

**1.** What would be good about knowing the answer to an important question beforehand? What might be really bad about this?

_____

_____

**2.** Chapter Nineteen is entitled, *Confession and Confusion.* Who do you think makes the confession? What do you think the confession involves?

_____

_____

## Vocabulary

**Circle the word that matches the meaning of the underlined word in each sentence.**

**1.** Melanie wanted Marshall to quit **pestering** her.

   a) bothering      b) questioning      c) stopping      d) loving

**2.** I don't think I've ever seen anyone as **enthusiastic** at a basketball game.

   a) talented      b) bored      c) eager      d) angry

**3.** Watching television is one way that she escaped from **reality**.

   a) escapism      b) realism      c) realty      d) parents

**4.** John was very **indignant** when the policeman accused him of lying.

   a) sorrowful      b) angry      c) talented      d) apologetic

**5.** April and Melanie were both **incredulous** at how well the game went with Toby and Ken.

   a) embarrassed   b) angry      c) unbelieving   d) fortunate

# Chapters Eighteen and Nineteen

## Part A

**1.** **Complete the paragraphs with the correct words from the chapters.**

_____. was upset because he had lost Security. Melanie assured him that
      **a**
Security wouldn't drown, because an octopus lives in _____. April's question to
                                                                    **b**
Thoth was, "When will I go _____ again?" When they checked the slip of paper
                                  **c**
the next day, an answer had been written on the _____ of the paper. Marshall
                                                        **d**
insisted on writing the next question: "Where is _____?"
                                                        **e**
_____ admitted to answering the first two questions. He was concerned
      **f**
about answering_____ question. When they arrived in Egypt, the answer to the
                        **g**
question was, "Look under the throne of _____". _____ denied writing
                                              **h**                      **i**
the answer.

**2.** **Which answer best describes...**

**a) Marshall?**

- ○ **A** bitter
- ○ **B** quiet
- ○ **C** sarcastic
- ○ **D** talkative

**b) what the others realized about Marshall?**

- ○ **A** He was immature.
- ○ **B** He was smart.
- ○ **C** He was moody.
- ○ **D** He was little.

**c) who was most worried about Marshall's question?**

- ○ **A** Melanie
- ○ **B** Toby
- ○ **C** April
- ○ **D** Marshall

**d) Toby, at the start of recess?**

- ○ **A** played tag football
- ○ **B** got into a fight
- ○ **C** pretended to turn his ankle
- ○ **D** received a detention

**e) Toby's outstanding talent according to his dad?**

- ○ **A** livening things up
- ○ **B** athletics
- ○ **C** getting out of work
- ○ **D** his imagination

**f) who Marshall thought took Security?**

- ○ **A** Isis
- ○ **B** The Professor
- ○ **C** Set
- ○ **D** Toby

# Chapters Eighteen and Nineteen

## Part B

**Answer the questions in complete sentences.**

**1.** Explain why the following quotation is an example of humor. **"Either Security was lost, or the world was coming to an end. It had to be serious!"**

_____

_____

**2.** Why do you think that in Chapter Eighteen, when the Egyptians returned to Egypt, they found that Marshall was "awfully little"?

_____

_____

**3.** Rephrase the answer to April's question in your own words, so the meaning of the answer is clearer: **"The best thing we can do is to make wherever we're lost in look as much like home as we can."**

_____

_____

**4.** Do you agree with April's statement, **"Some people think there's such a thing as too much excitement"**? Explain your answer.

_____

_____

**5.** Why did Toby think it necessary to pretend he was hurt in order to meet the girls at recess? What does this tell you about him?

_____

_____

**Journal Activity**

Imagine you have the opportunity of receiving the answer to an important question about the future. Write the question and a possible answer.

# Chapters Twenty and Twenty-one

**1.** What is your impression of the chapter title, *Fear Strikes*?  Is this an effective title?  Give reasons one way or the other.

_____

_____

**2.** Who do you think is guilty of killing the child?  Give reasons for your answer.

_____

_____

_____

## Vocabulary

**Circle the word that matches the meaning of the underlined word in each sentence.**

**1.** Marshall was a little less than **enthusiastic** to play the part of the boy Pharaoh.
   a) eager          b) determined          c) sad          d) talented

**2.** The teacher gave an **exasperated** sigh when Todd entered the room.
   a) desperate     b) annoyed          c) contented     d) relaxed

**3.** The story that the little boy told was very **vivid**.
   a) gory          b) unbelievable     c) picturesque     d) comical

**4.** When questioned by the police, the murdered woman's husband had a strong **alibi**.
   a) drink          b) excuse          c) bodyguard     d) lawyer

**5.** "I have told you a million times not to **exaggerate**", his mother told him.
   a) loan your belongings    b) lie to me    c) stretch the truth    d) leave the yard

# Chapters Twenty and Twenty-one

## Part A

**Put a check mark next to the answer that is most correct.**

**1. In Chapter Twenty, Marshall's babysitter was to be:**

- ○ **A** Melanie
- ○ **B** Elizabeth
- ○ **C** Toby
- ○ **D** April

**2. April decided to go back to Egypt to get:**

- ○ **A** her math book
- ○ **B** Security
- ○ **C** the oracle
- ○ **D** her wallet

**3. When April was attacked, who called out for help?**

- ○ **A** Marshall
- ○ **B** Toby
- ○ **C** a strange voice
- ○ **D** April

**4. According to Marshall, what color was the attacker's hair?**

- ○ **A** orange
- ○ **B** yellow
- ○ **C** blue
- ○ **D** black

**5. Who did the attacker work for?**

- ○ **A** Mr. Schmitt
- ○ **B** Caroline
- ○ **C** The Professor
- ○ **D** Inspector Grant

# Chapters Twenty and Twenty-one

**Part B**

## Answer the questions in complete sentences.

**1.** Do you agree with the statement, **"Being scared and chickening out were two different things"**?  Support your answer.

_____

_____

**2.** Explain what you think the author means by the statement, **"Imagination is a great thing in long dark hours, but it's a real curse in a dark alley"**.

_____

_____

**3.** At the end of Chapter Twenty-one, why do you think Marshall didn't need Security anymore?

_____

_____

**4.** The **climax** of a story usually takes place when the main problem of the story is solved.  What is the main problem in this novel?  When would you say the climax of The Egypt Game takes place?

_____

_____

**5.** What was odd about Marshall's description of the person who assaulted April?

_____

_____

**Journal Activity**

**Describe a time in your life when you were extremely frightened.  What happened and tell exactly how you felt.**

NAME: _____

# Chapters Twenty-two and Twenty-three

**Answer the questions in complete sentences.**

**1.** How do you think the Egyptians will feel now about returning to the Egypt Game in the storage yard?

_____

_____

**2.** What other games might the gang play in the storage yard? (Be as creative as April would be if asked this question!)

_____

## Vocabulary

**With a straight line, connect each word on the left with its meaning on the right.**

|  |  | |  |  |
|---|------|---|---------|--------|
| 1 | scarcely | | guess | A |
| 2 | consensus | | strain | B |
| 3 | particular | | hopeful | C |
| 4 | seclusion | | spangle | D |
| 5 | lair | | agreement | E |
| 6 | squat | | barely | F |
| 7 | tension | | edge | G |
| 8 | verge | | distinct | H |
| 9 | sequin | | den | I |
| 10 | speculate | | crude | J |
| 11 | optimistic | | alone | K |
| 12 | primitive | | crouch | L |

# Chapters Twenty-two and Twenty-three

## Part A

1. **Circle** **T** if the statement is **TRUE** or **F** if it is **FALSE**.

**T** **F** **a)** The day after all the excitement Toby found the land of Egypt all boarded up.

**T** **F** **b)** The other Egyptians were furious at April and Melanie for ruining their game.

**T** **F** **c)** The Professor hired Caroline to help him in his store.

**T** **F** **d)** The Professor's real name was Dr. Huxtabul.

**T** **F** **e)** April agreed to spend Christmas with her mother and Nick.

**T** **F** **f)** The mayor of the city gave everyone in the Egypt Gang a medal for bravery.

2. **Number the events from ❶ to ❻ in the order they occurred in the chapters.**

_____ **a)** The Professor shows April a couple of Egyptian relics.

_____ **b)** The Professor tells the Egyptians the story of his past.

_____ **c)** The Professor gives each of the children a key to the storage yard.

_____ **d)** The Egyptians believe that Egypt was lost and gone forever.

_____ **e)** Mr. Schmitt decides to sell out his store.

_____ **f)** April receives a letter from her mother.

# After You Read

## Chapters Twenty-two and Twenty-three

### Part B

**Answer the questions in complete sentences.**

1. The **denouement** of a story is defined as the events which take place after the story's climax. What main events described in these last two chapters make up the denouement of <u>The Egypt Game</u>?

   _____

   _____

2. The author refers to the Egypt Game as **"terrific . . . full of excitement and mystery and way-out imagining"**. Do you agree or disagree with the author's assessment? Explain your answer.

   _____

   _____

3. Were you satisfied with the conclusion of this novel? Do you think April's idea regarding changing the focus from Egyptians to Gypsies was good? Why or why not?

   _____

   _____

4. Explain why April's letter to her mother was so important in resolving April's feelings in this regard.

   _____

   _____

5. Put the following sentence in your own words: **"April and Melanie looked at each other and their eyes made extravagant comments"**.

**Journal Activity**

**Write a final reflection as to how you enjoyed this novel. What did you enjoy most about it? How would you have improved it?**

# Chapters 1 to 4

The Egypt Gang had a lot of fun writing messages in Egyptian hieroglyphics. Learning the alphabet of another people's written language can be a very exciting activity, especially hieroglyphics, which is like writing a picture puzzle.

**Your assignment is to write a message at least two sentences in length to another student in your class.**

The catch? The message must be either written in **Egyptian hieroglyphics** or in the letters of your own **unique alphabet**. In either case you are to put the letters of the alphabet on the back of your message so it can be deciphered.

Examples:  = arm and hand  = loaf of bread

---

# Chapters 5 to 8

In Chapter Seven the author makes the statement, "It occurred to her (April) that Caroline ought to know that you don't pick your friends just because they were handy – or even lonely. You picked them because you thought alike and were interested in the same things, the way she and Melanie were."

**First, explain why you either agree or disagree with this statement. Then tell about a time when you met someone who was to become a very good friend.**

Describe how you felt meeting this person and what it was like getting to know him or her. Was it at all similar to the author's description in this passage?

# Chapters 9 to 12

The novel mentions a poem that Melanie writes called <u>Hymn to Isis</u> which she created with just a bit of help from a book of Egyptian poetry. Many examples of Egyptian poetry have been passed down to us over the centuries. Many express most eloquently the thoughts and feelings of the people living during the time of the Pharaohs.

Here are the first four lines from an ancient Egyptian poem called **Changing Fortune**:

> *Once a fugitive fled from his terror,*
> *Now I am known, in the palace of the Pharaoh,*
> *Once a weary one fainted from hunger,*
> *Now I have bread to give to my neighbor.*

Imagine that you are living in Egypt during the time of the Pharaohs. **Write a poem of at least six lines in length describing your own feelings and/or adventures.** It can be any type of poem (rhyming or unrhyming, Haiku, Cinquain, etc.). Make sure that it has a distinctive Egyptian flavor.

- - - - - - - - - - - - - - - - - - - - - - - - - - - - - - - - - -

# Chapters 13 to 16

April seemed to put up with a lot from her mother, Dorthea. On more than one occasion April was badly hurt by her mother's careless and unfeeling regard of her.

**Put yourself in April's place for a few minutes and write a letter to your mother.**

In your letter you are to describe to Dorthea exactly how you feel about the way she has been treating you, especially since she left you with Caroline. Tell her why you feel this way and how Dorthea might change in order to be a more caring parent.

Your letter should be at least a half a page in length.

# Chapters 17 to 21

By this point in the novel we have met all the major characters of __The Egypt Game__.
Imagine now that you are the *casting director* of a major motion picture studio
who is about to make a feature length film of this novel.

> **Your task is to cast each of the following characters using only
> people (students, teachers, etc.) from your school.  For each
> character, write down who you have chosen to play the role and
> briefly explain why you selected that individual.**
>
> - April
> - The Professor
> - Dorthea
> - One other character of your choice
>
> - Melanie
> - Toby
> - Marshall

- - - - - - - - - - - - - - - - - - - - - - - - - - - - - - - - - - - - -

# Chapters 22 to 25

> **You be the critic!**
> Your assignment is to write a brief **book review** of __The Egypt Game__ for
> posting on a website such as www.amazon.com. This is an opportunity to
> share your opinion of the novel with other young people who are deciding
> whether to read the book or not.

**Your review should be at least two paragraphs in length.  One paragraph
should briefly describe the plot (without giving away the ending!)
The second paragraph should give your impression of the novel.**

When writing your impression, try to include one favorable comment and
one suggestion as to how the novel might be improved.

# Word Search

**Find all of the words in the word search. Words may be horizontal, vertical, or diagonal. A few may even be backwards. Look carefully!**

| | | | |
|---|---|---|---|
| ceremony | theory | momentum | incense |
| mysterious | triumph | tunic | ornaments |
| antique | monolith | prostrated | queasy |
| paralyzed | pharaoh | investigation | parallel |
| sacrificial | egyptologist | papyrus | disturbing |
| elaborate | university | rendezvous | reality |
| reproduction | hieroglyphics | dungeon | criminal |

| a | r | e | l | a | b | o | r | a | t | e | s | t | h | t | c | u | h |
|---|---|---|---|---|---|---|---|---|---|---|---|---|---|---|---|---|---|
| s | n | s | n | h | n | o | i | t | a | g | i | t | s | e | v | n | i |
| p | v | t | l | e | l | l | a | r | a | p | i | q | r | t | r | i | e |
| a | m | l | i | h | s | s | z | n | d | l | b | e | s | r | e | v | r |
| p | o | x | a | q | v | d | l | o | o | a | m | f | u | e | a | a | o |
| y | m | k | y | e | u | g | p | n | a | o | o | y | n | i | l | r | g |
| r | e | c | b | h | a | e | o | c | n | l | e | r | i | f | i | g | l |
| u | n | c | a | t | e | m | x | y | e | g | e | o | v | m | t | n | y |
| s | t | r | i | u | m | p | h | p | f | v | t | e | e | z | y | i | p |
| f | u | o | r | d | u | n | g | e | o | n | g | h | r | e | t | b | h |
| e | m | a | w | e | a | s | u | o | i | r | e | t | s | y | m | r | i |
| s | d | r | m | m | g | s | a | d | b | s | k | m | i | w | g | u | c |
| a | j | e | g | y | p | t | o | l | o | g | i | s | t | o | j | t | s |
| o | r | n | a | m | e | n | t | s | f | u | a | a | y | m | s | s | t |
| t | u | d | e | d | k | u | z | t | e | w | o | c | v | f | q | i | m |
| k | v | e | o | w | j | b | p | r | o | s | t | r | a | t | e | d | a |
| s | h | z | r | s | a | f | v | p | r | c | r | i | m | i | n | a | l |
| g | o | v | k | q | w | j | m | q | c | d | s | f | f | k | a | g | w |
| m | a | o | a | k | e | r | w | o | i | o | e | i | j | u | s | p | d |
| o | r | u | o | z | u | t | b | e | n | i | n | c | e | n | s | e | k |
| d | a | s | r | e | p | r | o | d | u | c | t | i | o | n | e | t | g |
| e | h | g | r | g | u | e | a | s | t | t | g | a | r | a | t | a | u |
| t | p | y | s | a | e | u | q | p | a | r | a | l | y | z | e | d | s |

NAME: _____

# Comprehension Quiz

**Answer the questions in complete sentences.**

**1.** What was there about the Professor that appealed to April at the beginning of the story?

_____

_____

**2.** What career was April's mother pursuing and whom did she leave April to live with?

_____

_____

**3.** Name one thing about April that made it difficult for other children to like her right away.

_____

**4.** What did Marshall keep with him at all times as a type of "security blanket"?

_____

**5.** Why did the girls decide to let Elizabeth join the Egypt Game even though she was only in grade four?

_____

_____

**6.** What tragedy in the neighborhood stopped the gang from playing the Egypt Game for awhile?

_____

_____

**7.** Who fell under suspicion as a result of the tragedy?

_____

_____

**SUBTOTAL:** /14

# Comprehension Quiz

**8.** What two boys joined the Egypt Game next? Which of the two was the most eager to participate?

_____

_____ ②

**9.** What was there about April's mother's letters that often caused April to be upset?

_____

_____ ②

**10.** What are hieroglyphics?

_____

_____ ②

**11.** Who did they have the Ceremony of the Dead in honor of?

_____ ②

**12.** Who provided answers to the first two oracles of Thoth? Who provided the last answer?

_____

_____ ②

**13.** What did April return to Egypt to get late one night when she was grabbed by the killer?

_____ ②

**14.** Who ended up saving April's life?

_____ ②

**15.** Where did April decide to spend Christmas?

_____ ②

**SUBTOTAL:** /16

**1.** Wore false eyelashes and an old fur stole; spoke with a haughty tone

**2.** Answers will vary

**3.** She is determined and not easily discouraged

**4.** Answers will vary

**5.** Answers will vary

---

**1.**
a) T
b) T
c) F
d) F
e) T
f) T

**2.**
a) 5
b) 4
c) 1
d) 2
e) 6
f) 3

---

**1.** Answers will vary

**2.** Answers will vary

**Vocabulary**

| | | | |
|---|---|---|---|
| 1 | J | | |
| 2 | K | | |
| 3 | H | | |
| 4 | A | | |
| 5 | B | | |
| 6 | I | | |
| 7 | L | | |
| 8 | G | | |
| 9 | F | | |
| 10 | E | | |
| 11 | C | | |
| 12 | D | | |

---

**1.** a) Answers will vary
b) Answers will vary

**2.** Answers will vary

**3.** An intriguing statement about the man's character and a hint of what might be to come

**4.** "his thin beard ... like dry moss" or "as blank as an empty well"

---

**1.** A

**2.** C

**3.** A

**4.** D

**5.** E

---

**1.** Answers will vary

**2.** Answers will vary

**Vocabulary**

1. dingy
2. taut
3. innovation
4. improvise
5. deadpan
6. exotic
7. vantage

**1.** Answers will vary

**2.** Answers will vary

**3.** Answers will vary

**4.** Answers will vary

**5.** Answers will vary

---

**1.**
a) Ross
b) child
c) killed
d) neighborhood
e) wait
f) sick
g) Professor
h) innocent
i) Halloween
j) disobedient
k) dangerous
l) Cleopatra
m) Security

**2.**
a) (A)  b) (B)
c) (C)  d) (C)

---

**1.** Answers will vary

**Vocabulary**

**Down:**
1. from
2. by
3. clamor
4. curious
5. mistake
6. noon
7. antique
11. ulu
12. chaperon
14. imitates
16. rapt
18. idol
21. owed
22. why
24. it

**Across:**
2. balcony
4. ceremony
8. dramas
9. omen
10. tunic
13. logical
15. Kurgan
17. smile
19. spread
20. Rosada
23. oily
25. haunt
26. dismay

---

**1.** Cliff-hanger – unknown sinister figure lurking in the background

**2.** Melanie was trying to mold April's personality so her fellow students would like her

**3.** Answers will vary

**4.** Answers will vary

**5.** Answers will vary

---

**1.**
a) Set
b) Marshamosis
c) February
d) Crocodile
e) four
f) poetry

**2.**
a) papyrus
b) Nefertiti
c) Security
d) Diana
e) Casa Rosada

---

**1.** Answers will vary

**2.** Answers will vary

**Vocabulary**
1. obliged
2. defiant
3. treacherous
4. sympathy
5. ferocious
6. delicate
7. ambushed

**Page 23**

1. Answers will vary

2. Dealing with people with tact and skill; Examples will vary

**Vocabulary**

1. unwieldy
2. haughty
3. convulsions
4. liable
5. together
6. prostrated
7. shred

**Page 24**

1. A
2. C
3. B
4. C
5. A

**Page 25**

1. The girls were beginning to be interested in boys

2. a) Answers will vary
   b) Answers will vary

3. Was aware that there was an eavesdropper to the Egypt Game

4. Answers will vary

5. Toby was interested; Ken went along reluctantly because of Toby's interest

**Page 26**

1. Answers will vary

2. Answers will vary

**Vocabulary**

1. aggravated
2. plain
3. hesitant
4. tragic
5. decipher
6. exchanged
7. inquiry

**Page 27**

1.
a) T
b) T
c) F
d) F
e) T
f) T

2.
a) 5
b) 6
c) 3
d) 1
e) 2
f) 4

**Page 28**

1. Answers will vary

2. Answers will vary (i.e. not being invited to the wedding, no time when April could move home)

3. Answers will vary

4. Answers will vary

5. Rubber spiders, snakes, bugs, a skull, tarantula, etc.

EZ✓

**1.** Contrast between 2 possibilities

**2.** He appeared very vulnerable

**3.** Answers will vary

**4.** Answers will vary

**5.** Didn't want to be teased by the other boys for playing with girls; His image was important to him

34

---

**1.**
a) Marshall
b) water
c) home
d) back
e) Security
f) Toby
g) Marshall's
h) Set
i) Toby

**2.**
a) B   b) D
c) B   d) C
e) A   f) C

33

---

**1.** Answers will vary

**2.** Answer will vary

**Vocabulary**

**1.** A
**2.** C
**3.** B
**4.** C
**5.** A

32

---

**1.** Probably didn't want to hurt anyone's feelings

**2.** He was self-conscious

**3.** In a saltwater bath

**4.** Elaborate ceremony; by telling the others that oracles used to work

**5.** Fasted and meditated for days

**6.** Answers will vary

31

---

**1.**
a) 40
b) Mother, Mourner
c) future
d) Thoth
e) thunder
f) Toby

**2.**
a) Prince Pete-ho-tep
b) Anubis
c) Aida
d) Ramose
e) Neferbeth
f) Horemheb

30

---

**1.** An authoritative prediction of the future (i.e., from a deity); Answers will vary

**2.** Something unexplained or secret that arouses curiosity or perplexes; Answers will vary

**Vocabulary**

Sentences will vary

29

**1.**
The Professor's story
– his gift of keys;
Dorthea's letter

**2.**
Answers will vary

**3.**
Answers will vary

**4.**
April realized she
could not depend
on her mother

**5.**
Answers will vary

---

**1.**
a) **T**
b) **F**
c) **F**
d) **F**
e) **F**
f) **F**

**2.**
a) 2
b) 5
c) 6
d) 1
e) 3
f) 4

---

**1.**
Answers will vary

**2.**
Answers will vary

**Vocabulary**
| | | | |
|---|---|---|---|
| **1** F | **2** E | **3** H | **4** K |
| **5** I | **6** L | **7** L | **8** B |
| **9** G | **10** A | **11** C | **12** J |

---

**1.**
Answers will vary

**2.**
Answers will vary

**3.**
He was growing up

**4.**
Problem – catching
the murderer;
Climax – when April
escapes from her
attacker and the
attacker is captured

**5.**
Was spotted and his
hair was orange

---

**1.** D

**2.** A

**3.** C

**4.**

**5.** A

A

---

**1.**
Answers will vary

**2.**
Answers will vary

**Vocabulary**
1. b
2. b
3. c
4. b
5. c

---

# Word Search Answers

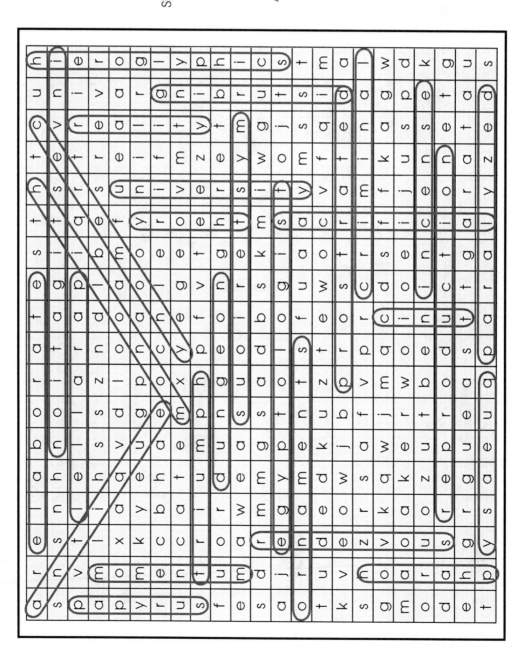

**1.** He was very quiet, mysterious

**2.** Acting, her grandmother, Caroline

**3.** She was outspoken, haughty

**4.** A stuffed octopus

**5.** She looked like Nefertiti

**6.** A child was murdered

**7.** The Professor

**8.** Ken and Toby; Toby was most eager

**9.** She wouldn't give April a date for returning home to live

**10.** Ancient Egyptian word pictures

**11.** Elizabeth's dead parakeet

**12.** Toby; The Professor

**13.** Her math book

**14.** The Professor

**15.** With her grandmother

**The Egypt Game CC2503**

# Publication Listing

Ask Your Dealer About Our Complete Line

## ENVIRONMENTAL STUDIES

| ITEM # | TITLE |
|--------|-------|
| | **MANAGING OUR WASTE SERIES** |
| CC5764 | Waste: At the Source |
| CC5765 | Prevention, Recycling & Conservation |
| CC5766 | Waste: The Global View |
| CC5767 | Waste Management Big Book |
| | **CLIMATE CHANGE SERIES** |
| CC5769 | Global Warming: Causes |
| CC5770 | Global Warming: Effects |
| CC5771 | Global Warming: Reduction |
| CC5772 | Global Warming Big Book |
| | **GLOBAL WATER SERIES** |
| CC5773 | Conservation: Fresh Water Resources |
| CC5774 | Conservation: Ocean Water Resources |
| CC5775 | Conservation: Waterway Habitats Resources |
| CC5776 | Water Conservation Big Book |
| | **CARBON FOOTPRINT SERIES** |
| CC5778 | Reducing Your Own Carbon Footprint |
| CC5779 | Reducing Your School's Carbon Footprint |
| CC5780 | Reducing Your Community's Carbon Footprint |
| CC5781 | Carbon Footprint Big Book |

## LANGUAGE ARTS

| ITEM # | TITLE |
|--------|-------|
| | **WRITING SKILLS SERIES** |
| CC1100 | How to Write a Paragraph |
| CC1101 | How to Write a Book Report |
| CC1102 | How to Write an Essay |
| CC1103 | Master Writing Big Book |
| | **READING SKILLS SERIES** |
| CC1116 | Reading Comprehension |
| CC1117 | Literary Devices |
| CC1118 | Critical Thinking |
| CC1119 | Master Reading Big Book |

## REGULAR & REMEDIAL EDUCATION

Reading Level 3-4  Grades 5-8

### SCIENCE

| ITEM # | TITLE |
|--------|-------|
| | **ECOLOGY & THE ENVIRONMENT SERIES** |
| CC4500 | Ecosystems |
| CC4501 | Classification & Adaptation |
| CC4502 | Cells |
| CC4503 | Ecology & The Environment Big Book |
| | **MATTER & ENERGY SERIES** |
| CC4504 | Properties of Matter |
| CC4505 | Atoms, Molecules & Elements |
| CC4506 | Energy |
| CC4507 | The Nature of Matter Big Book |
| | **FORCE & MOTION SERIES** |
| CC4508 | Force |
| CC4509 | Motion |
| CC4510 | Simple Machines |
| CC4511 | Force, Motion & Simple Machines Big Book |
| | **SPACE & BEYOND SERIES** |
| CC4512 | Space - Solar Systems |
| CC4513 | Space - Galaxies & The Universe |
| CC4514 | Space - Travel & Technology |
| CC4515 | Space Big Book |
| | **HUMAN BODY SERIES** |
| CC4516 | Cells, Skeletal & Muscular Systems |
| CC4517 | Nervous, Senses & Respiratory Systems |
| CC4518 | Circulatory, Digestive & Reproductive Systems |
| CC4519 | Human Body Big Book |

## SOCIAL STUDIES

| ITEM # | TITLE |
|--------|-------|
| | **NORTH AMERICAN GOVERNMENTS SERIES** |
| CC5757 | American Government |
| CC5758 | Canadian Government |
| CC5759 | Mexican Government |
| CC5760 | Governments of North America Big Book |
| | **WORLD GOVERNMENTS SERIES** |
| CC5761 | World Political Leaders |
| CC5762 | World Electoral Processes |
| CC5763 | Capitalism vs. Communism |
| CC5777 | World Politics Big Book |
| | **WORLD CONFLICT SERIES** |
| CC5500 | American Civil War |
| CC5511 | American Revolutionary War |
| CC5512 | American Wars Big Book |
| CC5501 | World War I |
| CC5502 | World War II |
| CC5503 | World Wars I & II Big Book |
| CC5505 | Korean War |
| CC5506 | Vietnam War |
| CC5507 | Korean & Vietnam Wars Big Book |
| CC5508 | Persian Gulf War (1990-1991) |
| CC5509 | Iraq War (2003-2010) |
| CC5510 | Gulf Wars Big Book |
| | **WORLD CONTINENTS SERIES** |
| CC5750 | North America |
| CC5751 | South America |
| CC5768 | The Americas Big Book |
| CC5752 | Europe |
| CC5753 | Africa |
| CC5754 | Asia |
| CC5755 | Australia |
| CC5756 | Antarctica |
| | **WORLD CONNECTIONS SERIES** |
| CC5782 | Culture, Society & Globalization |
| CC5783 | Economy & Globalization |
| CC5784 | Technology & Globalization |
| CC5785 | Globalization Big Book |
| | **MAPPING SKILLS SERIES** |
| CC5786 | Grades PK-2 Mapping Skills with Google Earth |
| CC5787 | Grades 3-5 Mapping Skills with Google Earth |
| CC5788 | Grades 6-8 Mapping Skills with Google Earth |
| CC5789 | Grades PK-8 Mapping Skills with Google Earth Big Book |

VISIT:

www.CLASSROOM COMPLETE PRESS.com

To view sample pages from each book

## LITERATURE KITS™

| ITEM # | TITLE |
|---|---|
| | **GRADES 1-2** |
| CC2100 | Curious George (H. A. Rey) |
| CC2101 | Paper Bag Princess (Robert N. Munsch) |
| CC2102 | Stone Soup (Marcia Brown) |
| CC2103 | The Very Hungry Caterpillar (Eric Carle) |
| CC2104 | Where the Wild Things Are (Maurice Sendak) |
| | **GRADES 3-4** |
| CC2300 | Babe: The Gallant Pig (Dick King-Smith) |
| CC2301 | Because of Winn-Dixie (Kate DiCamillo) |
| CC2302 | The Tale of Despereaux (Kate DiCamillo) |
| CC2303 | James and the Giant Peach (Roald Dahl) |
| CC2304 | Ramona Quimby, Age 8 (Beverly Cleary) |
| CC2305 | The Mouse and the Motorcycle (Beverly Cleary) |
| CC2306 | Charlotte's Web (E.B. White) |
| CC2307 | Owls in the Family (Farley Mowat) |
| CC2308 | Sarah, Plain and Tall (Patricia MacLachlan) |
| CC2309 | Matilda (Roald Dahl) |
| CC2310 | Charlie & The Chocolate Factory (Roald Dahl) |
| CC2311 | Frindle (Andrew Clements) |
| CC2312 | M.C. Higgins, the Great (Virginia Hamilton) |
| CC2313 | The Family Under The Bridge (N.S. Carlson) |
| | **GRADES 5-6** |
| CC2500 | Black Beauty (Anna Sewell) |
| CC2501 | Bridge to Terabithia (Katherine Paterson) |
| CC2502 | Bud, Not Buddy (Christopher Paul Curtis) |
| CC2503 | The Egypt Game (Zilpha Keatley Snyder) |
| CC2504 | The Great Gilly Hopkins (Katherine Paterson) |
| CC2505 | Holes (Louis Sachar) |
| CC2506 | Number the Stars (Lois Lowry) |
| CC2507 | The Sign of the Beaver (E.G. Speare) |
| CC2508 | The Whipping Boy (Sid Fleischman) |
| CC2509 | Island of the Blue Dolphins (Scott O'Dell) |
| CC2510 | Underground to Canada (Barbara Smucker) |
| CC2511 | Loser (Jerry Spinelli) |
| CC2512 | The Higher Power of Lucky (Susan Patron) |
| CC2513 | Kira-Kira (Cynthia Kadohata) |
| CC2514 | Dear Mr. Henshaw (Beverly Cleary) |
| CC2515 | The Summer of the Swans (Betsy Byars) |
| CC2516 | Shiloh (Phyllis Reynolds Naylor) |
| CC2517 | A Single Shard (Linda Sue Park) |
| CC2518 | Hoot (Carl Hiaasen) |
| CC2519 | Hatchet (Gary Paulsen) |
| CC2520 | The Giver (Lois Lowry) |
| CC2521 | The Graveyard Book (Neil Gaiman) |
| | **GRADES 7-8** |
| CC2700 | Cheaper by the Dozen (Frank B. Gilbreth) |
| CC2701 | The Miracle Worker (William Gibson) |
| CC2702 | The Red Pony (John Steinbeck) |
| CC2703 | Treasure Island (Robert Louis Stevenson) |
| CC2704 | Romeo & Juliet (William Shakespeare) |
| CC2705 | Crispin: The Cross of Lead (Avi) |

## REGULAR EDUCATION

• • • • • • • • • • • • • •

### LANGUAGE ARTS

| ITEM # | TITLE |
|---|---|
| | **READING RESPONSE FORMS SERIES** |
| CC1106 | Reading Response Forms: Grades 1-2 |
| CC1107 | Reading Response Forms: Grades 3-4 |
| CC1108 | Reading Response Forms: Grades 5-6 |
| CC1109 | Reading Response Forms Big Book: Grades 1-6 |
| | **WORD FAMILIES SERIES** |
| CC1110 | Word Families - Short Vowels: Grades PK-1 |
| CC1111 | Word Families - Long Vowels: Grades PK-1 |
| CC1112 | Word Families - Vowels Big Book: Grades K-1 |
| | **SIGHT & PICTURE WORDS SERIES** |
| CC1113 | High Frequency Sight Words: Grades PK-1 |
| CC1114 | High Frequency Picture Words: Grades PK-1 |
| CC1115 | Sight & Picture Words Big Book Grades PK-1 |

### INTERACTIVE WHITEBOARD SOFTWARE

| ITEM # | TITLE |
|---|---|
| | **CLIMATE CHANGE SERIES** |
| CC7747 | Global Warming: Causes Grades 3-8 |
| CC7748 | Global Warming: Effects Grades 3-8 |
| CC7749 | Global Warming: Reduction Grades 3-8 |
| CC7750 | Global Warming Big Box Grades 3-8 |
| | **HUMAN BODY SERIES** |
| CC7549 | Cells, Skeletal & Muscular Systems Grades 3-8 |
| CC7550 | Senses, Nervous & Respiratory Systems Grades 3-8 |
| CC7551 | Circulatory, Digestive & Reproductive Systems Grades 3-8 |
| CC7552 | Human Body Big Box Grades 3-8 |
| | **FORCE, MOTION & SIMPLE MACHINES SERIES** |
| CC7553 | Force Grades 3-8 |
| CC7554 | Motion Grades 3-8 |
| CC7555 | Simple Machines Grades 3-8 |
| CC7556 | Force, Motion & Simple Machines Big Box Grades 3-8 |
| | **WRITING SKILLS SERIES** |
| CC7104 | How to Write a Paragraph Grades 3-8 |
| CC7105 | How to Write a Book Report Grades 3-8 |
| CC7106 | How to Write an Essay Grades 3-8 |
| CC7107 | Master Writing Big Box Grades 3-8 |
| | **READING SKILLS SERIES** |
| CC7108 | Reading Comprehension Grades 3-8 |
| CC7109 | Literary Devices Grades 3-8 |
| CC7110 | Critical Thinking Grades 3-8 |
| CC7111 | Master Reading Big Box Grades 3-8 |
| | **SIGHT & PICTURE WORDS SERIES** |
| CC7100 | High Frequency Sight Words Grades PK-2 |
| CC7101 | High Frequency Picture Words Grades PK-2 |
| CC7102 | Sight & Picture Words Big Box Grades PK-2 |

## MATHEMATICS

| ITEM # | TITLE |
|---|---|
| | **PRINCIPLES & STANDARDS OF MATH SERIES** |
| CC3100 | Grades PK-2 Number & Operations Task Sheets |
| CC3101 | Grades PK-2 Algebra Task Sheets |
| CC3102 | Grades PK-2 Geometry Task Sheets |
| CC3103 | Grades PK-2 Measurement Task Sheets |
| CC3104 | Grades PK-2 Data Analysis & Probability Task Sheets |
| CC3105 | Grades PK-2 Five Strands of Math Big Book Task Sheets |
| CC3106 | Grades 3-5 Number & Operations Task Sheets |
| CC3107 | Grades 3-5 Algebra Task Sheets |
| CC3108 | Grades 3-5 Geometry Task Sheets |
| CC3109 | Grades 3-5 Measurement Task Sheets |
| CC3110 | Grades 3-5 Data Analysis & Probability Task Sheets |
| CC3111 | Grades 3-5 Five Strands of Math Big Book Task Sheets |
| CC3112 | Grades 6-8 Number & Operations Task Sheets |
| CC3113 | Grades 6-8 Algebra Task Sheets |
| CC3114 | Grades 6-8 Geometry Task Sheets |
| CC3115 | Grades 6-8 Measurement Task Sheets |
| CC3116 | Grades 6-8 Data Analysis & Probability Task Sheets |
| CC3117 | Grades 6-8 Five Strands of Math Big Book Task Sheets |
| | **PRINCIPLES & STANDARDS OF MATH SERIES** |
| CC3200 | Grades PK-2 Number & Operations Drill Sheets |
| CC3201 | Grades PK-2 Algebra Drill Sheets |
| CC3202 | Grades PK-2 Geometry Drill Sheets |
| CC3203 | Grades PK-2 Measurement Drill Sheets |
| CC3204 | Grades PK-2 Data Analysis & Probability Drill Sheets |
| CC3205 | Grades PK-2 Five Strands of Math Big Book Drill Sheets |
| CC3206 | Grades 3-5 Number & Operations Drill Sheets |
| CC3207 | Grades 3-5 Algebra Drill Sheets |
| CC3208 | Grades 3-5 Geometry Drill Sheets |
| CC3209 | Grades 3-5 Measurement Drill Sheets |
| CC3210 | Grades 3-5 Data Analysis & Probability Drill Sheets |
| CC3211 | Grades 3-5 Five Strands of Math Big Book Drill Sheets |
| CC3212 | Grades 6-8 Number & Operations Drill Sheets |
| CC3213 | Grades 6-8 Algebra Drill Sheets |
| CC3214 | Grades 6-8 Geometry Drill Sheets |
| CC3215 | Grades 6-8 Measurement Drill Sheets |
| CC3216 | Grades 6-8 Data Analysis & Probability Drill Sheets |
| CC3217 | Grades 6-8 Five Strands of Math Big Book Drill Sheets |
| | **PRINCIPLES & STANDARDS OF MATH SERIES** |
| CC3300 | Grades PK-2 Number & Operations Task & Drill Sheets |
| CC3301 | Grades PK-2 Algebra Task & Drill Sheets |
| CC3302 | Grades PK-2 Geometry Task & Drill Sheets |
| CC3303 | Grades PK-2 Measurement Task & Drill Sheets |
| CC3304 | Grades PK-2 Data Analysis & Probability Task & Drill |
| CC3306 | Grades 3-5 Number & Operations Task & Drill Sheets |
| CC3307 | Grades 3-5 Algebra Task & Drill Sheets |
| CC3308 | Grades 3-5 Geometry Task & Drill Sheets |
| CC3309 | Grades 3-5 Measurement Task & Drill Sheets |
| CC3310 | Grades 3-5 Data Analysis & Probability Task & Drill |
| CC3312 | Grades 6-8 Number & Operations Task & Drill Sheets |
| CC3313 | Grades 6-8 Algebra Task & Drill Sheets |
| CC3314 | Grades 6-8 Geometry Task & Drill Sheets |
| CC3315 | Grades 6-8 Measurement Task & Drill Sheets |
| CC3316 | Grades 6-8 Data Analysis & Probability Task & Drill |